Copyright Disclosure

TABLE OF CONTENTS

IMPLEMENTATION SCHEDULE

Below you will find Calm Classroom's recommended implementation schedules. Teach the techniques 2-3x/day in the classroom. Set up specific times for teaching Calm Classroom and post these times so students know when to expect the practice sessions. Facilitate the techniques at the beginning of the class period as part of the transition into to that particular period. After the Implementation Schedule has been completed, teach techniques that you and your students enjoy, or repeat the schedule from the beginning.

3x Daily Schedule:

	Morning Technique	Midday Technique	Afternoon Technique
Week 1	Body Scan	Feeling the Breath	I Am Calm
Week 2	Listening to Sound and Silence	Energy Hands	Standing Mountain
Week 3	Bell Focus	Shake and Relax	Seated Body Circles
Week 4	Deep Breathing	Music Scribble	Standing Side Bend
Week 5	External Counting	Two-Four Breathing	Quick Tense and Release
Week 6	Sun Breathing	Eye Palming	Out-Out-Out Breath
Week 7	Standing Back Bend	Eye Circles	Alternate Arm Breathing
Week 8	Butterfly Breathing	Dot Focus	Seated Twist
Week 9	Humming Focus	Enthusiastic Breathing	Standing Forward Bend
Week 10	Continuous Breathing	Breath Counting	Standing Body Circles
Week 11	Sitting in Stillness	Seated Back Bend	Haaaa Breathing
Week 12	Sniffing Breath	External Gazing	Seated Forward Bend
Week 13	Triangle Breathing	Magic Penny	Seated Side Bend
Week 14	Square Breathing	Metronome Focus	Seated Mountain

2x Daily Schedule:

	Morning Technique	Midday Technique
Week 1	Body Scan	Feeling the Breath
Week 2	I Am Calm	Listening to Sound and Silence
Week 3	Energy Hands	Standing Mountain
Week 4	Bell Focus	Shake and Relax
Week 5	Seated Body Circles	Deep Breathing
Week 6	Music Scribble	Standing Side Bend
Week 7	External Counting	Two-Four Breathing
Week 8	Quick Tense and Release	Sun Breathing
Week 9	Eye Palming	Out-Out-Out Breath
Week 10	Standing Back Bend	Eye Circles
Week 11	Alternate Arm Breathing	Butterfly Breathing
Week 12	Dot Focus	Seated Twist
Week 13	Humming Focus	Enthusiastic Breathing
Week 14	Standing Forward Bend	Continuous Breathing
Week 15	Breath Counting	Standing Body Circles
Week 16	Sitting in Stillness	Seated Back Bend
Week 17	Haaaa Breathing	Sniffing Breath
Week 18	External Gazing	Seated Forward Bend
Week 19	Triangle Breathing	Magic Penny
Week 20	Seated Side Bend	Square Breathing
Week 21	Metronome Focus	Seated Mountain

OVERVIEW

We live in an age where multitasking is a valued skill, cell phones and social media reign supreme, and our minds seem to focus on the past or future, often unaware of the present moment unfolding before us. Faced with innumerable social, emotional, and environmental challenges, teachers and students alike are battling chronic stress, anxiety and depression.

Enter Calm Classroom.

"Calm Classroom makes my mind feel like it's got more strength than my body."

"I get real calm and it puts me in a mindset where I can just focus and do my work."

"Since I began using Calm Classroom, I've seen myself change. I have become more mature, and I am taking responsibility for my actions."

Calm Classroom is a program that uses simple research-based mindfulness techniques to help students and teachers develop self-awareness, mental focus, and inner calm. The program provides students and staff with the tools to more effectively manage stress, regulate their emotions, and in turn lead more productive, well-balanced lives. By seamlessly integrating these techniques into the classroom culture, Calm Classroom cultivates a more mindful school climate, helping students to foster attitudes of respect and kindness towards themselves and others.

The Calm Classroom program is composed of breathing, stretching, relaxation and focusing techniques. Each scripted technique takes three minutes to implement. Teachers lead these practices three scheduled times each day in their classrooms, and are encouraged to utilize the techniques when naturally appropriate. Calm Classroom can be implemented school-wide, in individual classrooms, or during counseling sessions with students.

IMPLEMENTATION

When to Teach Calm Classroom

Teachers can post a Calm Classroom schedule so that students know when to expect the techniques. We recommend delivering Calm Classroom:

- Two to three times each day
- During regular classroom transitions after students are already seated and quiet
- Any time students need to calm down
- Any time students need to feel more alert and energized
- Before a test
- After a classroom upset

Tips for Teaching

The Calm Classroom manual contains scripted techniques that can be facilitated by teachers and students. When facilitating the techniques:

- Pause at the end of each line, take one full breath before moving on
- Slow your pacing down, but remain natural
- Remain still
- Keep tone soft and soothing

By taking time to breathe between instructions, the leader can experience the benefits of the technique while leading it.

The Calm Classroom audio recordings can be found in the digital manuals to help you preview, learn, and facilitate the techniques. Once familiar, teachers and students are encouraged to lead the techniques directly from the scripts without the aid of the audio recordings.

Materials

Focusing Chime: The focusing chime is used to facilitate the "Bell Focus" technique in the manual. It can also be used to calmly begin or conclude any Calm Classroom technique.

Student Ambassador Program and Posters: This program is designed to empower students by giving them simple responsibilities that prepare the classroom to transition into and out of Calm Classroom. Students will:

- Remind the teacher that it is time for Calm Classroom
- Put the "Do Not Enter" sign on the door
- Turn off the lights
- Take the "Do Not Enter" sign off the door
- Turn on the lights and mark the Calm Calendar

The "Student Ambassador Responsibilities" poster lists all of these tasks.

Calm Classroom Schedule Sign: Teachers will use this sign to set a daily schedule for when they plan to teach Calm Classroom. For example, "after reading, after lunch, before math". The sign supports teachers and students in remembering to teach the program three times a day.

Do Not Enter Sign: The "Do Not Enter" sign reminds school staff and students not to enter the classroom while Calm Classroom is being delivered.

Calm Calendar: The purpose of the Calm Calendar is to provide the class with a way to formalize their practice of Calm Classroom by keeping track of how often they are practicing each month. The student ambassador will mark an "x" or sign their initials on the calendar after each Calm Classroom session, offering a visual representation of their progress. Students can enjoy a feeling of accomplishment upon seeing a week of completed techniques.

Calm Classroom "Any Time, Any Place" Program: This campaign is designed to assist students in understanding the relevance of Calm Classroom outside of the classroom by presenting them with three techniques that they can practice at any time, any place. Teachers will use Practice Posters to guide a discussion around how Calm Classroom can be used, for example:

- When waking up or going to bed
- When in the car or on the bus
- When feeling stressed, nervous, angry, or sad

Practice Posters: These three posters are displayed in the classroom to remind students that they can practice the Calm Classroom techniques on their own anytime they need them, in and outside of school, without distracting others. The Practice Poster techniques include: "I Am Calm," "Feeling the Breath," and "Listening to Sound." Teachers focus on one poster every Friday, encouraging students to practice the technique over the weekend and report back on Monday.

Student Leaders Program: This program allows students to take ownership over Calm Classroom by teaching the techniques to their peers during class. Student leaders will gain valuable leadership, presentation, and reading skills by learning to effectively deliver Calm Classroom techniques to their classmates.

INTRODUCING THE CURRICULUM

Private Introductions

Meet privately with students who may disrupt the process before introducing the curriculum to the rest of the class. Lead these students in one or more techniques so they know what to expect. Give permission for students to sit quietly if they do not want to participate.

General Classroom Introduction

Explain that students will learn new ways to relax and energize the body, control their breathing, concentrate the mind and be more aware of thoughts and feelings. Calm Classroom techniques will help students:

- Calm themselves down when they are experiencing a strong emotion
- Remain relaxed and focused during tests
- Become better problem-solvers
- Think before they react
- Improve physical health
- Stay energized and engaged during the school day

Include a brief explanation and discussion on each type of technique:

Breathing

Practicing breathing techniques is one of the best ways to relieve stress and relax. Deep breathing increases the supply of oxygen to your brain, promoting a state of calm. Taking short, quick breaths can help us to feel more alert. Breathing techniques connect you to your physical body, helping to take your awareness off of your worries and quiet the mind.

Explore breathing and how it changes depending on what we are thinking, feeling, or doing:

- How do you breathe when you are afraid, angry or nervous?
- How do you breathe when you are relaxed and calm?

Focus

We can improve our ability to focus by practicing paying attention to one thing at a time. When you notice your mind wandering, gently bring your attention back to the object of focus, whether it is the breath, sounds in your environment, or a physical sensation.

Explore the difference between being focused and distracted:

- When I am talking to you do you sometimes think about other things? How does this affect your ability to learn?
- Why is it easier to learn when we are focused and relaxed?

Relaxation

Learning to relax your body is an important skill that will help you to deal with stress and improve your overall wellbeing. The body's relaxation response lowers stress levels in the brain, leading to increased energy, motivation and capacity to learn.

Explore what it is like to feel stressed:

- What does it feel like when your mind and body are stressed?
- How does stress affect your mood and relationship with others?
- When you notice you feel afraid, angry, or nervous what do you do to help yourself feel more calm and relaxed?

Stretching

Stretching helps free our bodies of any tightness caused by stress. When we stretch, fresh blood and oxygen are carried to the muscles. This restores our energy levels and helps us to relax.

Explore stretching and how it makes the body feel:

- How does your body feel after you have been sitting at your desk or the computer for a long time? What parts of your body ache or are stiff?
- How does feeling tired affect your ability to stay focused?
- What can you do to help your body feel better?

What to Expect

A small minority of students may at first feel uncomfortable when practicing the techniques. Student resistance might include:

- Refusing to close eyes
- Slouching or falling asleep

- Refusing to participate
- Disturbing other students
- Laughing
- Excessive moving
- Talking or making noise

It is okay if a few students do not fully participate. It is not okay if students disturb the classroom. Students who choose not to close their eyes can instead gaze at a point or small object on their desk. Continue to invite these students to close their eyes.

Disruptive students can be managed within the pre-existing disciplinary structure of the classroom. Should a student's behavior warrant a one-on-one discussion, go over the manual with them, explain the benefits, and if necessary provide alternatives, such as: allowing students to sit quietly without disturbing others.

Peer Leaders

The best way for students to integrate the skills taught in Calm Classroom is to teach a technique themselves. Give students the opportunity to lead the class in a Calm Classroom technique. This will empower them to be more active participants in the program and take ownership over the class's progress.

Conclusion

The benefits of Calm Classroom are directly related to the consistency, quantity, and quality of the practice. Regularity will produce the most effective results.

The most important factor in the success of the program is the teacher's commitment to utilizing the techniques and practicing along with the students.

Calm Classroom supports the gradual development of empowered, self-aware individuals and encourages peace within ourselves and our communities.

BREATHING

DEEP BREATHING

Introduction – Modeling:

We are going to practice a Calm Classroom technique today called "Deep Breathing." As you breathe in through your nose, you will expand your belly, then your rib cage, and finally your chest as your lungs fill with air. As you breathe out through your nose, you will contract your chest, your rib cage, then your belly, as you feel the air moving out. In order to help guide your breathing, I will repeat the phrase, "Breathe in, one, two, three, hold. Breathe out, three, two, one, hold."

Technique Start:

We are going to practice "Deep Breathing."

Sit up straight and comfortably in your chair.

Rest your hands on your desk or in your lap.

Close your eyes or leave them open.

Feel your feet flat on the floor.

Relax your shoulders back and down.

Let your whole body be still.

Feel the air moving in and out of your nose.
[Wait 10 seconds]

Remember, when you breathe in, you will fill your lungs completely.

Make each breath slow, smooth, and deep.

Now, breathe in as I count, 1....2....3....hold.
Breathe out as I count, 3....2....1....hold.

Breathe in, 1....2....3....hold.
Breathe out, 3....2....1....hold.

Breathe in, 1....2....3....hold.
Breathe out, 3....2....1....hold.

DEEP BREATHING (cont.)

Breathe in, 1....2....3....hold.
Breathe out, 3....2....1....hold.

Now, breathe naturally and relax.

Feel the air moving in and out of your nose.
[Wait 20-30 seconds]

Now, take a deep breath in, hold and exhale slowly.

Notice how you feel.
[Wait 10 seconds]

Open your eyes if they were closed.

SUN BREATHING

Introduction – Modeling:

We are going to practice a Calm Classroom technique today called "Sun Breathing." This technique combines physical movement and breathing. As you breathe in through your nose, you will lift both of your arms straight up over your head, like this *[teacher lifts their arms up while breathing in]*. As you breathe out through your nose, you will lower your arms, like this *[teacher breathes out and lowers their arms]*.

Technique Start:

We are going to practice "Sun Breathing."

Sit up straight and comfortably in your chair.

Rest your hands on your desk or in your lap.

Close your eyes or leave them open.

Feel your feet flat on the floor.

Relax your shoulders back and down.

Let your whole body be still.

Feel the air moving in and out of your nose.
[Wait 10 seconds]

Now, inhale deeply through your nose and stretch your arms straight over your head with your palms facing each other. Hold. Slowly lower your arms and exhale.

Inhale stretch up, hold, exhale, arms down.

Inhale stretch up, hold, exhale, arms down.

Inhale stretch up, hold, exhale, arms down.

Now, rest your hands on your desk or in your lap.

SUN BREATHING (cont.)

Feel the air moving in and out of your nose.
[Wait 20-30 seconds]

Now, take a deep breath in, hold and exhale slowly.

Notice how you feel.
[Wait 10 seconds]

Open your eyes if they were closed.

BUTTERFLY BREATHING

Introduction – Modeling:

We are going to practice a Calm Classroom technique today called "Butterfly Breathing." Butterfly Breathing has two parts. First, you will lace your fingers under your chin and press the palms of your hands together. *[Teacher interlaces their fingers underneath their chin, palms together.]* Then, breathe in through your nose as you lift your elbows up and out to the sides. *[Teacher lifts their elbows up and out to sides while breathing in.]* When you breathe out through your nose, you will bring your elbows back down toward each other. *[Teacher lowers elbows down toward each other.]*

Technique Start:

We are going to practice "Butterfly Breathing."

Sit up straight and comfortably in your chair.

Rest your hands on your desk or in your lap.

Close your eyes or leave them open.

Feel your feet flat on the floor.

Relax your shoulders back and down.

Let your whole body be still.

Feel the air moving in and out of your nose.
[Wait 10 seconds]

Interlace your fingers and hands and place them under your chin.

Breathe in through your nose and lift your elbows up and out to the sides. Breathe out through your nose and lower your elbows down toward each other.

Breathe in, lift your elbows up, breathe out, lower your elbows down.

Breathe in, elbows up, breathe out, elbows down.

Breathe in, up, breathe out, down.

BUTTERFLY BREATHING (cont.)

Breathe in, up, breathe out, down.

Slowly lower your hands to rest on your desk or in your lap.

Feel the air moving in and out of your nose.
[Wait 20-30 seconds]

Now, take a deep breath in, hold and exhale slowly.

Notice how you feel.
[Wait 10 seconds]

Open your eyes if they were closed.

ALTERNATE ARM BREATHING

Introduction – Modeling:

We are going to practice a Calm Classroom technique today called "Alternate Arm Breathing." Start by putting your palms together in front of your chest, like this *[teacher places hands together in front of their chest]*. As you breathe in through your nose, you will lift one arm straight up overhead, like this *[teacher lifts one arm up while breathing in]*. As you breathe out through your nose, you will lower your arm down and bring your hands back together at your chest, like this *[teacher breathes out and lowers their arm, bringing their hands back together]*. Then we will do the same thing with the opposite arm. *[Teacher lifts the other arm up while breathing in, and lowers the arm while breathing out.]* We will repeat this technique, alternating arms as we go.

Technique Start:

We are going to practice "Alternate Arm Breathing."

Sit up straight and comfortably in your chair.

Rest your hands on your desk or in your lap.

Close your eyes or leave them open.

Feel your feet flat on the floor.

Relax your shoulders back and down.

Let your whole body be still.

Feel the air moving in and out of your nose.
[Wait 10 seconds]

Place your hands together.

Now, inhale and slowly reach your right arm straight up over your head.
Exhale, and slowly lower your right hand to meet your left hand.

Inhale, reach your left arm straight up over your head.
Exhale, lower your left hand to meet your right hand.

Inhale, reach your right arm over your head.

ALTERNATE ARM BREATHING (cont.)

Exhale, lower your right hand to meet your left hand.

Inhale, reach your left arm over your head.
Exhale, lower your left hand to meet your right hand.

Slowly lower your hands to rest on your desk or in your lap.

Feel the air moving in and out of your nose.
[Wait 20-30 seconds]

Now, take a deep breath in, hold and exhale slowly.

Notice how you feel.
[Wait 10 seconds]

Open your eyes if they were closed.

CONTINUOUS BREATHING

Introduction – Modeling:

Today we are going to practice a technique called "Continuous Breathing." You will breathe in through your nose as I count to two, and breathe out through your nose as I count to two. I will repeat the phrase "inhale, one, two, exhale, one, two" to help guide your breathing pattern. Do not pause between inhaling and exhaling.

Technique Start:

We are going to practice "Continuous Breathing."

Sit up straight and comfortably in your chair.

Rest your hands on your desk or in your lap.

Close your eyes or leave them open.

Feel your feet flat on the floor.

Relax your shoulders back and down.

Let your whole body be still.

Feel the air moving in and out of your nose.
[Wait 10 seconds]

Remember to breathe deeply, continuously, and quickly, without pausing.

Now, inhale, one, two, exhale, one, two.
Inhale, one, two, exhale, one, two.
Inhale, one, two, exhale, one, two.
Inhale, one, two, exhale, one, two.
Inhale, one, two, exhale, one, two.
Inhale, one, two, exhale, one, two.

Now, breathe naturally and relax.

Feel the air moving in and out of your nose.
[Wait 20-30 seconds]

CONTINUOUS BREATHING (cont.)

Now, take a deep breath in, hold and exhale slowly.

Notice how you feel.
[Wait 10 seconds]

Open your eyes if they were closed.

TWO-FOUR BREATHING

Introduction – Modeling:

We are going to practice a Calm Classroom technique today called "Two-Four Breathing." You will breathe in through your nose as I count to two, and breathe out through your nose as I count to four. In order to help guide your breathing, I will repeat the phrase, "Inhale, one, two, hold. Exhale, one, two, three, four, hold."

Technique Start:

We are going to practice "Two-Four Breathing."

Sit up straight and comfortably in your chair.

Rest your hands on your desk or in your lap.

Close your eyes or leave them open.

Feel your feet flat on the floor.

Relax your shoulders back and down.

Let your whole body be still.

Feel the air moving in and out of your nose.
[Wait 10 seconds]

Remember you are going to exhale twice as long as you inhale.

Now, inhale, 1....2....hold.
Exhale, 1....2....3....4....hold.

Inhale, 1....2....hold.
Exhale, 1....2....3....4....hold.

Inhale, 1....2....hold.
Exhale, 1....2....3....4....hold.

Inhale, 1....2....hold.
Exhale, 1....2....3....4....hold.

TWO-FOUR BREATHING (cont.)

Inhale, 1....2....hold.
Exhale, 1....2....3....4....hold.

Now, breathe naturally and relax.

Feel the air moving in and out of your nose.
[Wait 20-30 seconds]

Now, take a deep breath in, hold and exhale slowly.

Notice how you feel.
[Wait 10 seconds]

Open your eyes if they were closed.

ENTHUSIASTIC BREATHING

Introduction – Modeling:

We are going to practice "Enthusiastic Breathing." You will reach both your arms straight up over your head as you breathe in quickly through your nose. *[Teacher reaches arms over head while breathing in through nose.]* You will make fists, and quickly pull your elbows down as you forcefully breathe out through your mouth. *[Teacher demonstrates pulling arms down in synch with a vigorous exhalation.]*

Technique Start:

We are going to practice "Enthusiastic Breathing."

Sit up straight and comfortably in your chair.

Rest your hands on your desk or in your lap.

Close your eyes or leave them open.

Feel your feet flat on the floor.

Relax your shoulders back and down.

Let your whole body be still.

Feel the air moving in and out of your nose.
[Wait 10 seconds]

Now, reach your arms straight up and breathe in through your nose. Make fists, pull your elbows down and breathe out forcefully through your mouth.

Breathe in, reach up. Breathe out, pull down. Keep going.

Breathe in, breathe out.

Breathe in, breathe out.

Breathe in, breathe out.

Slowly lower your hands to rest on your desk or in your lap.

ENTHUSIASTIC BREATHING (cont.)

Feel the air moving in and out of your nose.
[Wait 20-30 seconds]

Now, take a deep breath in, hold and exhale slowly.

Notice how you feel.
[Wait 10 seconds]

Open your eyes if they were closed.

OUT-OUT-OUT BREATH

Introduction – Modeling:

We are going to practice a Calm Classroom technique today called "Out-Out-Out Breath." You will be taking one deep breath in and three quick mini breaths out. Take a deep breath in through your nose, like this *[teacher demonstrates breathing in through their nose]*. Then you will blow the air out through your mouth as you breathe out three times, like this *[teacher demonstrates breathing out with three mini exhalations]*.

Technique Start:

We are going to practice "Out-Out-Out Breath."

Sit up straight and comfortably in your chair.

Rest your hands on your desk or in your lap.

Close your eyes or leave them open.

Feel your feet flat on the floor.

Relax your shoulders back and down.

Let your whole body be still.

Feel the air moving in and out of your nose.
[Wait 10 seconds]

Now, breathe in slowly through your nose, hold. Breathe out three mini exhalations through your mouth.

Slowly breathe in through your nose, hold.
Breathe out three times.

Slowly breathe in through your nose, hold.
Breathe out three times.

Slowly breathe in through your nose, hold.
Breathe out three times.

OUT-OUT-OUT BREATH (cont.)

Now, breathe naturally and relax.

Feel the air moving in and out of your nose.
[Wait 20-30 seconds]

Now, take a deep breath in, hold and exhale slowly.

Notice how you feel.
[Wait 10 seconds]

Open your eyes if they were closed.

SNIFFING BREATH

Introduction – Modeling:

We are going to practice "Sniffing Breath." You will inhale through your nose for three short, quick "sniffs" until your lungs are full, like this *[teacher takes three quick sniffing breaths]*. Then you will exhale slowly through your nose, like this *[teacher exhales slowly through nose]*.

Technique Start:

We are going to practice "Sniffing Breath."

Sit up straight and comfortably in your chair.

Rest your hands on your desk or in your lap.

Close your eyes or leave them open.

Feel your feet flat on the floor.

Relax your shoulders back and down.

Let your whole body be still.

Feel the air moving in and out of your nose.
[Wait 10 seconds]

Begin by exhaling the air gently out of your lungs.

Now inhale three short, quick sniffs until your lungs are full. Hold. Exhale, slowly.

Inhale three quick sniffs, hold. Exhale, slowly.

Inhale three quick sniffs, hold. Exhale, slowly.

Inhale three quick sniffs, hold. Exhale, slowly.

Now, breathe naturally and relax.

Feel the air moving in and out of your nose.
[Wait 20-30 seconds]

SNIFFING BREATH (cont.)

Now, take a deep breath in, hold and exhale slowly.

Notice how you feel.
[Wait 10 seconds]

Open your eyes if they were closed.

TRIANGLE BREATHING

Introduction – Modeling:

We are going to practice "Triangle Breathing." This technique has three parts. You will breathe in through your nose as I count to three. Then you will hold your breath as I count to three. Finally, you will exhale as I count to three. To help guide your breathing pattern, I will repeat the phrase "Inhale, one, two, three. Hold, one, two, three. Exhale, one, two, three."

Technique Start:

We are going to practice "Triangle Breathing."

Sit up straight and comfortably in your chair.

Rest your hands on your desk or in your lap.

Close your eyes or leave them open.

Feel your feet flat on the floor.

Relax your shoulders back and down.

Let your whole body be still.

Feel the air moving in and out of your nose.
[Wait 10 seconds]

Begin by exhaling the air gently out of your lungs.

Now, inhale, 1....2....3.   Hold, 1....2....3.   Exhale, 1....2....3.

Inhale, 1....2....3.   Hold, 1....2....3.   Exhale, 1....2....3.

Inhale, 1....2....3.   Hold, 1....2....3.   Exhale, 1....2....3.

Inhale, 1....2....3.   Hold, 1....2....3.   Exhale, 1....2....3.

Now, breathe naturally and relax.

Feel the air moving in and out of your nose.

TRIANGLE BREATHING (cont.)

[Wait 20-30 seconds]

Now, take a deep breath in, hold and exhale slowly.

Notice how you feel.
[Wait 10 seconds]

Open your eyes if they were closed.

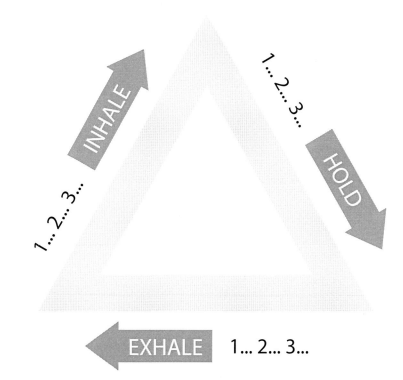

SQUARE BREATHING

Introduction – Modeling:

We are going to practice "Square Breathing." This technique has four parts. You will breathe in, hold, exhale, and hold again. To help guide your breathing pattern, I will repeat the phrase, "Inhale, one, two, three, four. Hold, one, two, three, four. Exhale, one, two, three, four. Hold, one, two, three, four."

Technique Start:

We are going to practice "Square Breathing."

Sit up straight and comfortably in your chair.

Rest your hands on your desk or in your lap.

Close your eyes or leave them open.

Feel your feet flat on the floor.

Relax your shoulders back and down.

Let your whole body be still.

Feel the air moving in and out of your nose.
[Wait 10 seconds]

Begin by exhaling the air gently out of your lungs.

Now, inhale, 1....2....3....4   Hold, 1....2....3....4   Exhale, 1....2....3....4   Hold, 1....2....3....4

Inhale, 1....2....3....4   Hold, 1....2....3....4   Exhale, 1....2....3....4   Hold, 1....2....3....4

Inhale, 1....2....3....4   Hold, 1....2....3....4   Exhale, 1....2....3....4   Hold, 1....2....3....4

Inhale, 1....2....3....4   Hold, 1....2....3....4   Exhale, 1....2....3....4   Hold, 1....2....3....4

Now, breathe naturally and relax.

Feel the air moving in and out of your nose.
[Wait 20-30 seconds]

SQUARE BREATHING (cont.)

Now, take a deep breath in, hold and exhale slowly.

Notice how you feel.
[Wait 10 seconds]

Open your eyes if they were closed.

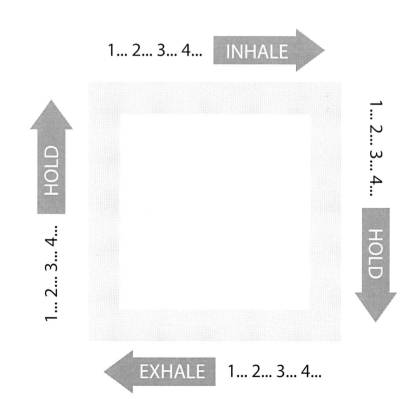

"HAAAA" BREATHING

Introduction – Modeling:

We are going to practice a Calm Classroom technique today called "Haaaa Breathing." You are going to take a deep breath in through your nose, like this *[teacher breathes in through their nose].* Then you will breathe out very slowly through your mouth while making a soft "haaaa" sound. *[Teacher breathes out slowly, making a "haaaa" sound.]*

Technique Start:

We are going to practice "Haaaa Breathing."

Sit up straight and comfortably in your chair.

Rest your hands on your desk or in your lap.

Close your eyes or leave them open.

Feel your feet flat on the floor.

Relax your shoulders back and down.

Let your whole body be still.

Feel the air moving in and out of your nose.
[Wait 10 seconds]

Remember, when you breathe out through your mouth you will make a "haaaa" sound.

Now, take a deep breath in through your nose. Hold.
Breathe out slowly, "haaaa."

Take a deep breath in through your nose. Hold.
Breathe out slowly, "haaaa."

Take a deep breath in through your nose. Hold.
Breathe out slowly, "haaaa."

Now, breathe naturally and relax.

"HAAAA" BREATHING (cont.)

Feel the air moving in and out of your nose.
[Wait 20-30 seconds]

Now, take a deep breath in, hold and exhale slowly.

Notice how you feel.
[Wait 10 seconds]

Open your eyes if they were closed.

FOCUS

BELL FOCUS

Introduction – Modeling:

We are going to practice a Calm Classroom technique today called "Bell Focus." When I ring the bell, you will focus all of your attention on the sound until it fades away completely and then you will listen to the silence in the room. If your mind starts thinking about something other than the sound of the bell, try to bring your mind back to the sound. The bell sounds like this *[teacher rings bell]*. I will ring the bell three times.

Technique Start:

We are going to practice "Bell Focus."

You will place your attention on the sound of the bell.

Sit up straight and comfortably in your chair.

Rest your hands on your desk or in your lap.

Close your eyes or leave them open.

Feel your feet flat on the floor.

Relax your shoulders back and down.

Let your whole body be still.

Feel the air moving in and out of your nose.
[Wait 10 seconds]

When the bell rings, place your attention on the sound without moving your body. If you notice any thoughts passing through your mind, let them float away and bring your attention back to the sound of the bell.

[Ring bell three times. Each time the bell rings, wait for the bell to stop ringing completely before continuing.]

Bring your attention back to your breathing.
[Wait 10 seconds]

BELL FOCUS (cont.)

Now, take a deep breath in, hold and exhale slowly.

Notice how you feel.
[Wait 10 seconds]

Open your eyes if they were closed.

[Use Calm Classroom Portal audio or your own chime]

DOT FOCUS

Introduction – Modeling:

Today we are going to practice a Calm Classroom technique called "Dot Focus." You will focus your eyes on the dot on your card. *[Teacher holds up the dot card.]* If you notice your eyes moving away from the dot, bring your gaze back to it. After looking at the dot for one minute, you will close your eyes and look for an image of a white dot on the inside of your forehead.

Technique Start:

We are going to practice "Dot Focus."

Place the dot card on your desk.

Sit up straight and comfortably in your chair.

Rest your hands on your desk or in your lap.

Feel your feet flat on the floor.

Relax your shoulders back and down.

Let your whole body be still.

Feel the air moving in and out of your nose.
[Wait 10 seconds]

Pick up the dot card and begin to look at the dot.

Keep your gaze steady.

Keep your eyes relaxed.

If you notice your eyes moving away from the dot, bring your gaze back to it.

Continue focusing on the dot.

Notice when your eyes blink.

Be aware of your breathing.

DOT FOCUS (cont.)

Keep your attention on the dot.

Now, close your eyes and watch for an internal white image of the dot on the inside of your forehead. It is alright if you don't see an internal white image.
[Wait 10 seconds]

Feel the air moving in and out of your nose.
[Wait 20-30 seconds]

Now, take a deep breath in, hold and exhale slowly.

Notice how you feel.
[Wait 10 seconds]

Slowly open your eyes.

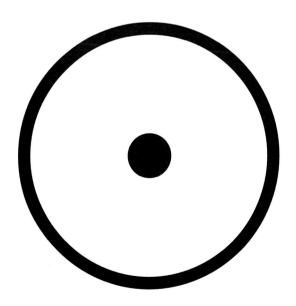

"I AM CALM"

Introduction – Modeling:

Today we are going to practice a technique called "I Am Calm." As you inhale through your nose, you will silently repeat the word "I," and as you exhale through your nose, you will silently repeat the words "Am Calm." As you breathe, try to focus your attention on just these three words.

Technique Start:

We are going to practice "I Am Calm."

Sit up straight and comfortably in your chair.

Rest your hands on your desk or in your lap.

Close your eyes or leave them open.

Feel your feet flat on the floor.

Relax your shoulders back and down.

Let your whole body be still.

Breathe naturally and relax.

As you breathe in through your nose, notice the feeling of the air moving in. As you breathe out through your nose, notice the feeling of the air moving out.
[Wait 10 seconds]

Now, as you feel the air moving in through your nose, silently repeat the *word*, "I." As you feel the air moving out through your nose, silently repeat the words, "Am Calm."

Breathe in and silently repeat, " I. " Breathe out and silently repeat, "Am Calm."

Continue "I Am Calm"on your own.
[Wait 20-30 seconds]

Now, take a deep breath in, hold and exhale slowly.

"I AM CALM" (cont.)

Notice how you feel.
[Wait 10 seconds]

Open your eyes if they were closed.

EXTERNAL GAZING

Introduction – Modeling:

Today we are going to practice "External Gazing." Choose an object to focus on. You can choose a pencil, a book, an eraser, or any other small object. Then, put that object on your desk. *[Teacher waits until everyone has chosen an object.]* When we begin, you will allow your eyes to relax while you focus on the object in front of you. Try your best to ignore everything else around you.

Technique Start:

We are going to practice "External Gazing."

[Choose objects if you haven't already.]

Sit up straight and comfortably in your chair.

Rest your hands on your desk or in your lap.

Feel your feet flat on the floor.

Relax your shoulders back and down.

Breathe naturally and relax.

Let your whole body be still.

Begin to look at the object you have chosen.
[Wait 10 seconds]

If you notice your eyes moving away from the object, bring your gaze back to it.
[Wait 10 seconds]

If you become aware of any thoughts passing through your mind, let them float away and bring your attention back to your object.

Continue external gazing on your own.
[Wait 20-30 seconds]

Now, close your eyes or leave them open.

EXTERNAL GAZING (cont.)

Let your eyes relax.

Feel the air moving in and out of your nose.
[Wait 20-30 seconds]

Now, take a deep breath in, hold and exhale slowly.

Notice how you feel.
[Wait 10 seconds]

Open your eyes if they were closed.

MAGIC PENNY

Introduction – Modeling:

We are going to practice a Calm Classroom technique today called "Magic Penny." I will hand out one penny to each of you. Then you will pick it up and press it on the center of your forehead, like this. *[Teacher presses a penny to the center of their forehead.]* If your forehead is relaxed, the penny will stay where you put it. During this technique, focus on the feeling of the penny on your forehead. If the penny falls off, focus on the spot where the penny was, and see if you can still feel the sensation of the penny on your forehead. We will begin once everyone has a penny. *[Teacher passes out pennies, or has a student assist.]*

Technique Start:

We are going to practice "Magic Penny."

Sit up straight and comfortably in your chair.

Place the penny on the center of your forehead.

Rest your hands on your desk or in your lap.

Close your eyes or leave them open.

Feel your feet flat on the floor.

Let your whole body be still.

Bring your attention to the penny on your forehead.

As you breathe in through your nose, notice the feeling of the penny.

As you breathe out through your nose, notice the feeling of the penny.

If your attention moves away from the feeling of the penny, gently bring it back.

Continue to notice your breathing and the feeling of the penny.
[Wait 20-30 seconds]

Now, carefully take the penny off of your forehead.

Rest your hands on your desk or in your lap.

MAGIC PENNY (cont.)

Feel the air moving in and out of your nose.
[Wait 20-30 seconds]

Now, take a deep breath in, hold and exhale slowly.

Notice how you feel.
[Wait 10 seconds]

Open your eyes if they were closed.

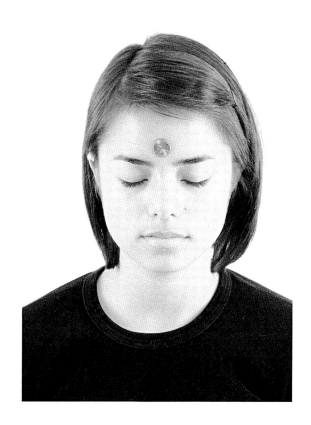

MUSIC SCRIBBLE

Introduction – Modeling:

Today we are going to practice a Calm Classroom technique called "Music Scribble." During this technique, I will play music. While the music plays, you will keep your body still but let your hand move as you use a pen or pencil to scribble on your paper. Try to move your hand in time with the music. When the music stops, you will stop scribbling. After the technique is over, you will be able to share what you have drawn and see how others have interpreted the music.

Technique Start:

We are going to practice "Music Scribble."

Place a sheet of paper and a pen or pencil on your desk.

Sit up straight and comfortably in your chair.

Rest your hands on your desk or in your lap.

Feel your feet flat on the floor.

Relax your shoulders back and down.

Let your whole body be still.

Feel the air moving gently in and out of your nose.
[Wait 10 seconds]

Pick up your pen or pencil.

Close your eyes or leave them open.

[Play Music]

Listen to the music without moving your body.
[Wait 10 seconds]

Now, begin to scribble to the music.

Keep your attention focused on the sound of the music and the feeling of your hand moving on the paper.

MUSIC SCRIBBLE (cont.)

[Music ends]

Slowly place your pen or pencil on your desk.

Rest your hands on your desk or in your lap.

Feel the air moving in and out of your nose.
[Wait 20-30 seconds]

Now, take a deep breath in, hold and exhale slowly.

Notice how you feel.
[Wait 10 seconds]

Open your eyes if they were closed.

[Use Calm Classroom Portal audio or choose your own music]

LISTENING TO SOUND AND SILENCE

Introduction – Modeling:

Today we are going to practice a technique called "Listening to Sound and Silence." You will be keeping your body still as you listen to the sound and silence in the room. Pay attention to whatever sounds are happening around you. You may notice many sounds, only a few, or none at all. If your mind starts thinking about something else, bring your attention back to the sound and silence in the room.

Technique Start:

We are going to practice "Listening to Sound and Silence."

Sit up straight and comfortably in your chair.

Rest your hands on your desk or in your lap.

Close your eyes or leave them open.

Feel your feet flat on the floor.

Relax your shoulders back and down.

Let your whole body be still.

Feel the air moving gently in and out of your nose.
[Wait 10 seconds]

As you become aware of sound in the room, listen to it without moving your body.
[Wait 10 seconds]

As you become aware of silence in the room, listen to it without moving your body.
[Wait 10 seconds]

If you notice any thoughts passing through your mind, let them float away and bring your attention back to the sound and silence.
[Wait 20-30 seconds]

Feel the air moving in and out of your nose.
[Wait 20-30 seconds]

Now, take a deep breath in, hold and exhale slowly.

Notice how you feel.
[Wait 10 seconds]

Open your eyes if they were closed.

EXTERNAL COUNTING

Introduction – Modeling:

Today we are going to practice a Calm Classroom technique called "External Counting." I will be counting backwards from ten to one, gradually lengthening the pause between each number. As I count, you will focus on both the sound of my voice, and the silence in between the numbers.

Technique Start:

We are going to practice "External Counting."

Sit up straight and comfortably in your chair.

Rest your hands on your desk or in your lap.

Close your eyes or leave them open.

Feel your feet flat on the floor.

Relax your shoulders back and down.

Let your whole body be still.

Feel the air moving gently in and out of your nose.
[Wait 10 seconds]

Listen to my voice as I slowly count down from ten to one.

Notice the increasing amount of silence between the numbers.

10...9....8.....7......6......5.......4........3.........2..........1

[Create longer periods of silence between each number as you count down]

Feel the air moving in and out of your nose.
[Wait 20-30 seconds]

Now, take a deep breath in, hold and exhale slowly.

Notice how you feel.
[Wait 10 seconds]

Open your eyes if they were closed.

ENERGY HANDS

Introduction – Modeling:

We are going to practice a technique today called "Energy Hands." You will be rubbing your hands together, like this *[teacher rubs hands together]*. Then, you will be clapping your hands, like this *[teacher claps hands]*. When you stop clapping and rubbing your hands, you will hold them apart, like this *[teacher holds hands about five inches apart, palms facing each other]*. You will try to feel the energy between your hands.

Technique Start:

We are going to practice "Energy Hands."

Sit up straight and comfortably in your chair.

Feel your feet flat on the floor.

Bring your hands together and quickly rub them.

Rub your hands together faster.

Keep rubbing.

Now, clap your hands.

Clap your hands faster.

Now, quickly rub your hands together again.

Feel the heat in your palms.

Listen to the sound of your hands rubbing together.

Stop rubbing your hands.

Hold your hands about five inches apart with your palms facing each other.

Close your eyes or leave them open.

Keep your hands and fingers relaxed.

ENERGY HANDS (cont.)

Notice the feeling between your hands.

Slowly move your hands apart like you are holding a basketball.

Slowly move your hands toward each other like you are holding a baseball.

Now, move your hands together until they touch.

Rest your hands on your desk or in your lap.

Feel the air moving in and out of your nose. *[Wait 20-30 seconds]*

Now, take a deep breath in, hold and exhale slowly.

Notice how you feel.
[Wait 10 seconds]

Open your eyes if they were closed.

BREATH COUNTING

Introduction – Modeling:

We are going to practice a Calm Classroom technique called "Breath Counting." You are going to silently count each breath as you breathe in and out. First, you will breathe in and say 'one' to yourself. Then, you will breathe out and say 'two,' and so on. I will guide your first few breaths, then you will count silently on your own.

Technique Start:

We are going to practice "Breath Counting."

Sit up straight and comfortably in your chair.

Rest your hands on your desk or in your lap.

Close your eyes or leave them open.

Feel your feet flat on the floor.

Relax your shoulders back and down.

Let your whole body be still.

Breathe naturally and relax.

As you breathe in through your nose, notice the feeling of the air moving in. As you breathe out through your nose, notice the feeling of the air moving out.

Focus on the feeling of the air moving in and out of your nose.
[Wait 10 seconds]

Now, feel your breath moving in, and silently count "one."

Feel your breath moving out, and silently count "two."

Breathe in, count "three."

Breathe out, count "four."

Continue counting on your own.

BREATH COUNTING (cont.)

[Wait 20-30 seconds]

Now, take a deep breath in, hold and exhale slowly.

Notice how you feel.
[Wait 10 seconds]

Open your eyes if they were closed.

METRONOME FOCUS

Introduction – Modeling:

We are going to practice a Calm Classroom technique today called "Metronome Focus." A metronome is a device that counts out a beat at a steady pace. While the metronome ticks, you will focus all of your attention on the sound it makes, and on the silence in-between the ticks.

Technique Start:

We are going to practice "Metronome Focus."

Sit up straight and comfortably in your chair.

Rest your hands on your desk or in your lap.

Close your eyes or leave them open.

Feel your feet flat on the floor.

Relax your shoulders back and down.

Let your whole body be still.

Feel the air moving in and out of your nose.
[Wait 10 seconds]

Listen to the sound of the metronome and the silent gaps in-between the sound.

[Play metronome for 20-30 seconds]

Bring your attention back to your breath.
[Wait 10 seconds]

Now, take a deep breath in, hold and exhale slowly.

Notice how you feel.
[Wait 10 seconds]

Open your eyes if they were closed.

[Use Calm Classroom Portal audio or your own metronome]

46

SITTING IN STILLNESS

Introduction – Modeling:

We are going to practice a Calm Classroom technique today called "Sitting in Stillness." You will be holding your body still as you focus your attention on different parts of your body.

Technique Start:

We are going to practice "Sitting in Stillness."

Sit up straight and comfortably in your chair.

Rest your hands on your desk or in your lap.

Close your eyes or leave them open.

Feel your feet flat on the floor.

Relax your shoulders back and down.

Let your whole body be still.
[Wait 10 seconds]

Bring your attention to your head.

Bring your attention to your shoulders.

Bring your attention to your hands.

Bring your attention to your knees.

Bring your attention to your feet.

Feel the stillness in your whole body.

Feel the air moving in and out of your nose.
[Wait 20-30 seconds]

Now, take a deep breath in, hold and exhale slowly.

Notice how you feel.
[Wait 10 seconds]

Open your eyes if they were closed.

EYE CIRCLES

Introduction – Modeling:

We are going to practice a Calm Classroom technique today called "Eye Circles." This technique will help us to strengthen our eye muscles. You will be keeping your body still as you move your eyes in circles. As I say "up, right, down, and left" you will move your eyes in that direction. Then we will change directions.

Technique Start:

We are going to practice "Eye Circles."

Sit up straight and comfortably in your chair.

Rest your hands on your desk or in your lap.

Feel your feet flat on the floor.

Relax your shoulders back and down.

Let your whole body be still.

Look at one spot straight in front of you.

Without moving your head, look up, look right, look down, look left.

Look up, look right, look down, look left.

Look up, look right, look down, look left.

Now, change directions.

Without moving your head, look up, look left, look down, look right.

Look up, look left, look down, look right.

Look up, look left, look down, look right.

Now, look at one spot straight in front of you.

EYE CIRCLES (cont.)

Close your eyes or leave them open .

Let your eye muscles relax.
[Wait 10 seconds]

Feel the air moving in and out of your nose.
[Wait 20-30 seconds]

Now, take a deep breath in, hold and exhale slowly.

Notice how you feel.
[Wait 10 seconds]

Open your eyes if they were closed.

HUMMING FOCUS

Introduction – Modeling:

We are going to practice a Calm Classroom technique today called "Humming Focus." You will take in a deep breath through your nose, and as you exhale you will make a humming noise, like this *[teacher makes a steady humming sound]*. You will focus on the feeling of your throat, mouth, and forehead as you hum. On the third breath, you will put your hands over your ears, like this. *[Teacher puts their palms over their ears.]* Then when you hum, you will notice how the sound changes in your ears.

Technique Start:

We are going to practice "Humming Focus."

Sit up straight and comfortably in your chair.

Rest your hands on your desk or in your lap.

Close your eyes or leave them open.

Feel your feet flat on the floor.

Relax your shoulders back and down.

Let your whole body be still.

Feel the air moving in and out of your nose.
[Wait 10 seconds]

Remember to pay attention to the physical feelings in your throat, mouth, and forehead as you hum.

Take a deep breath in through your nose, hold, exhale, mmmmmmmmmmmmm.

Take a deep breath in through your nose, hold, exhale, mmmmmmmmmmmmm.

Now, place your palms over your ears.

Take a deep breath in through your nose, hold, and exhale, mmmmmmmmmmmmm.

Rest your hands on your desk or in your lap.

Feel the air moving in and out of your nose.

HUMMING FOCUS (cont.)

[Wait 20-30 seconds]

Now, take a deep breath in, hold and exhale slowly.

Notice how you feel.
[Wait 10 seconds]

Open your eyes if they were closed.

FEELING THE BREATH

Introduction – Modeling:

We are going to practice a technique today called "Feeling the Breath." You will focus your attention on the feeling of your breath as the air moves in and out of your body. As you breathe in through your nose, focus on the feeling of the air moving in. As you breathe out through your nose, focus on the feeling of the air moving out.

Technique Start:

We are going to practice "Feeling the Breath."

Sit up straight and comfortably in your chair.

Rest your hands on your desk or in your lap.

Close your eyes or leave them open.

Feel your feet flat on the floor.

Relax your shoulders back and down.

Let your whole body be still.

Breathe naturally and relax.

As you breathe in through your nose, notice the feeling of the air moving in. As you breathe out through your nose, notice the feeling of the air moving out.
[Wait 10 seconds]

If you become aware of any thoughts passing through your mind, let them float away and bring your attention back to the feeling of your breath.
[Wait 20-30 seconds]

Now, take a deep breath in, hold and exhale slowly.

Notice how you feel.
[Wait 10 seconds]

Open your eyes if they were closed.

RELAXATION

QUICK TENSE AND RELEASE

Introduction – Modeling:

We are going to practice a Calm Classroom technique today called "Quick Tense and Release." First, you will extend your arms and legs out in front of you, like this *[teacher extends arms and legs out while seated]*. Then you will make fists and tighten your hands and arm muscles. *[Teacher demonstrates.]* Then you will tighten your feet and leg muscles. *[Teacher demonstrates.]* Then you will take a deep breath in through your nose as you tighten even more, and exhale through your mouth as you drop your arms and legs and let them completely relax. *[Teacher drops arms and legs.]*

Technique Start:

We are going to practice "Quick Tense and Release."

Sit up straight and comfortably in your chair.

Rest your hands on your desk or in your lap.

Close your eyes or leave them open.

Feel your feet flat on the floor.

Relax your shoulders back and down.

Let your whole body be still.

Feel the air moving in and out of your nose.
[Wait 10 seconds]

Lift and straighten your legs out in front of you.

Lift and straighten your arms out in front of you.

Tighten your feet and legs.

Make fists and tighten your hands and arms.

Take a deep breath in and tighten your legs and arms even more.

Now, exhale through your mouth and drop your legs and arms.

Relax your whole body.

QUICK TENSE AND RELEASE (cont.)

Lift and straighten your legs out in front of you.

Lift and straighten your arms out in front of you.

Tighten your feet and legs.

Make fists and tighten your hands and arms.

Take a deep breath in and tighten your legs and arms even more.

Now, exhale through your mouth and drop your legs and arms.

Relax your whole body.

Lift and straighten your legs out in front of you.

Lift and straighten your arms out in front of you.

Tighten your feet and legs.

Make fists and tighten your hands and arms.

Take a deep breath in and tighten your legs and arms even more.

Now, exhale through your mouth and drop your legs and arms.

Relax your whole body.

Feel the air moving in and out of your nose.
[Wait 20-30 seconds]

Now, take a deep breath in, hold and exhale slowly.

Notice how you feel.
[Wait 10 seconds]

Open your eyes if they were closed.

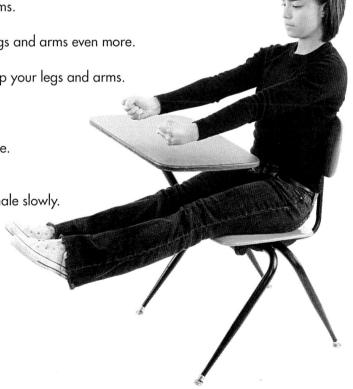

SHAKE AND RELAX

Introduction – Modeling:

We are going to practice a Calm Classroom technique today called "Shake and Relax." You will be shaking and moving different parts of your body. You will pay attention to how your body feels as you shake and move. Then, you will stop and hold your body still. You will pay attention to how your body feels as you completely relax.

Technique Start:

We are going to practice "Shake and Relax."

Stand up straight and comfortably.

Feel your feet flat on the floor.

Rest your arms by your sides.

Relax your shoulders back and down.

Let your whole body be still.

Feel the air moving in and out of your nose.
[Wait 10 seconds]

Start shaking your right hand and arm.

Watch your hand and arm shaking.

Now, close your eyes or leave them open and feel your hand and arm shaking.

Shake your left hand and arm.

Shake both arms.

Shake your shoulders.

Shake your right leg.

Shake your left leg.

SHAKE AND RELAX (cont.)

Carefully shake your head.

Now, shake your whole body.

Shake even more!
[Wait 10 seconds]

Now, stop shaking!

Rest your arms by your sides and hold your body still.

Feel the energy in your arms.

Feel the energy in your hands and fingers.

Notice the energy in your whole body.

Feel the air moving in and out of your nose.
[Wait 20-30 seconds]

Now, take a deep breath in, hold and exhale slowly.

Notice how you feel.
[Wait 10 seconds]

Open your eyes if they were closed.

BODY SCAN

Introduction – Modeling:

We are going to practice a Calm Classroom technique today called "Body Scan." You will be holding your body still as you pay attention to how different parts of your body feel. For example, bring your attention to your feet and see if you can feel them without moving them. *[Teacher waits for five seconds.]* You will be relaxing and noticing how each part of your body feels as I guide your attention to it.

Technique Start:

We are going to practice "Body Scan."

Rest your head on your desk or sit up straight and comfortably in your chair.

Close your eyes or leave them open.

Feel your feet flat on the floor.

Feel the air moving in and out of your nose.
[Wait 10 seconds]

If you notice any thoughts passing through your mind, let them float away.

Without moving them, feel and relax your feet.

Bring your attention to your legs. Relax your legs.

Move your attention to your belly. Relax your belly.

Notice your lower back. Relax your lower back.

Bring your attention to your shoulders. Relax your shoulders.

Feel your arms, hands, and fingers relaxing.

Feel your jaw, eyes, and forehead relaxing.

Notice your whole body.

Let your whole body relax.
[Wait 20-30 seconds]

Now, slowly wiggle your toes.

Slowly wiggle your fingers.

BODY SCAN (cont.)

Keeping your eyes closed, gently sit up straight and comfortably in your chair.

Now, take a deep breath in, hold and exhale slowly.

Notice how you feel.
[Wait 10 seconds]

Open your eyes if they were closed.

EYE PALMING

Introduction – Modeling:

We are going to practice a Calm Classroom technique today called "Eye Palming." You will be rubbing your palms together until your hands are warm. *[Teacher rubs palms together.]* Then, you will place your palms over your eyes so no light comes in, like this *[teacher puts palms over eyes for a few seconds to demonstrate]*. You will notice the warmth as you let your forehead, your eyes, and your face relax.

Technique Start:

We are going to practice "Eye Palming."

Sit up straight and comfortably in your chair.

Rest your hands on your desk or in your lap.

Close your eyes or leave them open.

Feel your feet flat on the floor.

Relax your shoulders back and down.

Breathe naturally and relax.

Bring your palms together.

Rub your palms together quickly.

Listen to the sound of your hands rubbing together.

Feel the heat and energy in your palms.

Keep rubbing your palms together.

Rub your palms together faster.

Keep your palms together and stop rubbing.

Now, place your palms over your eyes, with your fingertips resting at the top of your forehead.

EYE PALMING (cont.)

Notice the warmth and darkness.

Let your eyes relax.

Let your forehead relax.

Let your whole face relax.
[Wait 10 seconds]

Now, rest your hands on your desk or in your lap.

Feel the air moving in and out of your nose.
[Wait 20-30 seconds]

Now, take a deep breath in, hold and exhale slowly.

Notice how you feel.
[Wait 10 seconds]

Open your eyes if they were closed.

STRETCHING

SEATED MOUNTAIN

Introduction – Modeling:

We are going to practice a Calm Classroom technique today called "Seated Mountain." While sitting upright in your chair, you will raise your arms above your head with your palms facing each other, like this *[teacher demonstrates]*. With your elbows straight and your shoulders relaxed, you will sit up as tall as possible.

Technique Start:

We are going to practice "Seated Mountain."

Sit up straight and comfortably in your chair.

Feel your feet flat on the floor.

Rest your hands on your desk or in your lap.

Relax your shoulders back and down.

Let your whole body be still.

Stretch your arms straight over your head with your palms facing each other.

Close your eyes or leave them open.

Feel the air moving in and out of your nose.

Keep stretching up with your elbows and fingers straight.
[Wait 10 seconds]

Slowly lower your arms and rest your hands on your desk or in your lap.

Bring your attention back to your breathing.
[Wait 20-30 seconds]

Now, take a deep breath in, hold and exhale slowly.

SEATED MOUNTAIN (cont.)

Notice how you feel.

[Wait 10 seconds]

Open your eyes if they were closed.

STANDING MOUNTAIN

Introduction – Modeling:

We are going to practice a Calm Classroom technique today called "Standing Mountain." While standing next to your desk with your feet together, you will raise your arms above your head and place your palms together, like this *[teacher demonstrates]*. With your elbows straight and your shoulders relaxed, you will stand up as tall as possible.

Technique Start:

We are going to practice "Standing Mountain."

Stand up straight and comfortably with your feet together.

Feel your feet flat on the floor.

Rest your arms by your sides.

Relax your shoulders back and down.

Let your whole body be still.

Stretch your arms straight over your head with your palms facing each other.

Close your eyes or leave them open.

Bring your hands together.

Feel the air moving in and out of your nose.

Keep stretching up with your elbows and fingers straight.
[Wait 10 seconds]

Slowly lower your arms.

Rest your hands by your sides.

Bring your attention back to your breathing.
[Wait 20-30 seconds]

STANDING MOUNTAIN (cont.)

Now, take a deep breath in, hold and exhale slowly.

Notice how you feel.
[Wait 10 seconds]

Open your eyes if they were closed.

SEATED FORWARD BEND

Introduction – Modeling:

We are going to practice a Calm Classroom technique today called "Seated Forward Bend." While sitting upright in your chair, you will raise your arms above your head with your palms facing each other, like this *[teacher demonstrates]*. Then you will carefully bend forward, reaching your hands toward your feet. *[Teacher demonstrates.]* Then, you will sit up slowly and raise your arms back above your head with your palms facing each other. Finally, you will lower your arms and rest your hands in your lap.

Technique Start:

We are going to practice "Seated Forward Bend."

Sit up straight and comfortably in your chair.

Feel your feet flat on the floor.

Rest your hands in your lap.

Relax your shoulders back and down.

Let your whole body be still.

Stretch your arms straight over your head with your palms facing each other.

Now, carefully bend forward.

Reach for your legs, ankles or feet, and be comfortable.

Close your eyes or leave them open.

Relax your head, neck and face.

Feel the air moving in and out of your nose.
[Wait 20-30 seconds]

Now, slowly sit up and stretch your arms straight over your head with your palms facing each other.

Lower your arms and rest your hands in your lap.

SEATED FORWARD BEND (cont.)

Bring your attention back to your breathing.
[Wait 10 seconds]

Now, take a deep breath in, hold and exhale slowly.

Notice how you feel.
[Wait 10 seconds]

Open your eyes if they were closed.

SEATED BACK BEND

Introduction – Modeling:

We are going to practice a Calm Classroom technique today called "Seated Back Bend." While sitting upright in your chair, you will raise your arms above your head with your palms facing each other, like this *[teacher demonstrates]*. Then you will carefully bend backward, lifting up your chin and extending your back. *[Teacher demonstrates.]* Then, you will sit up slowly, with your arms still above your head. Finally, you will lower your arms and rest your hands in your lap. *[Teacher demonstrates.]*

Technique Start:

We are going to practice "Seated Back Bend."

Sit up straight and comfortably in your chair.

Feel your feet flat on the floor.

Rest your hands on your desk or in your lap.

Relax your shoulders back and down.

Let your whole body be still.

Stretch your arms straight over your head with your palms facing each other.

Keep your elbows straight.

Carefully bend backward.

Lift your chin.

Be comfortable.

Close your eyes or leave them open.

Feel the air moving in and out of your nose.
[Wait 20-30 seconds]

Now, slowly sit up and stretch your arms straight over your head.

SEATED BACK BEND (cont.)

Lower your arms and rest your hands on your desk or in your lap.

Bring your attention back to your breathing.
[Wait 10 seconds]

Now, take a deep breath in, hold and exhale slowly.

Notice how you feel.
[Wait 10 seconds]

Open your eyes if they were closed.

STANDING FORWARD BEND

Introduction – Modeling:

We are going to practice a Calm Classroom technique today called "Standing Forward Bend." While standing next to your desk with your feet together, you will raise your arms above your head with your palms facing each other, like this *[teacher demonstrates]*. Then you will carefully bend forward, reaching your hands toward your feet. *[Teacher demonstrates.]* Then, you will roll your body up slowly and raise your arms above your head with your palms facing each other. Finally, you will lower your arms and rest your hands by your sides. *[Teacher demonstrates.]*

Technique Start:

We are going to practice "Standing Forward Bend."

Stand up straight and comfortably with your feet together.

Feel your feet flat on the floor.

Rest your arms by your sides.

Relax your shoulders back and down.

Let your whole body be still.

Stretch your arms straight over your head with your palms facing each other.

Now, carefully bend forward.

Reach for your legs, ankles or feet, and be comfortable.

Close your eyes or leave them open.

Let your head and neck hang down.

Feel the stretch in the back of your legs.
[Wait 20-30 seconds]

Now, roll your body up and stretch your arms straight over your head with your palms facing each other.

STANDING FORWARD BEND (cont.)

Lower your arms and rest your hands by your sides.

Feel the air moving in and out of your nose.
[Wait 10 seconds]

Now, take a deep breath in, hold and exhale slowly.

Notice how you feel.
[Wait 10 seconds]

Open your eyes if they were closed.

STANDING BACK BEND

Introduction – Modeling:

We are going to practice a Calm Classroom technique today called "Standing Back Bend." While standing next to your desk with your feet together, you will place your hands on your lower back with your fingertips pointing down, like this *[teacher demonstrates]*. Then you will bend slightly backward, lifting your chin and using your hands to support your back. *[Teacher demonstrates.]* Then, you will slowly lift your body straight up, and lower your hands by your sides. *[Teacher demonstrates.]*

Technique Start:

We are going to practice "Standing Back Bend."

Stand up straight and comfortably with your feet together.

Feel your feet flat on the floor.

Rest your arms by your sides.

Relax your shoulders back and down.

Let your whole body be still.

Place your hands on your lower back with your fingertips pointing down.

Carefully bend backward.

Lift your chin.

Close your eyes or leave them open.

Be comfortable.

Feel the stretch.
[Wait 20-30 seconds]

Now, bring your body straight up.

Lower your arms and rest your hands by your sides.

STANDING BACK BEND (cont.)

Feel the air moving in and out of your nose.
[Wait 10 seconds]

Now, take a deep breath in, hold and exhale slowly.

Notice how you feel.
[Wait 10 seconds]

Open your eyes if they were closed.

SEATED SIDE BEND

Introduction – Modeling:

We are going to practice a Calm Classroom technique today called "Seated Side Bend." While sitting upright in your chair, you will raise your arms above your head with your fingers interlaced and your index fingers pointing upward, like this *[teacher demonstrates]*. Then you will carefully bend to one side. *[Teacher demonstrates.]* Next, you will straighten your back and return to the center. *[Teacher demonstrates.]* Then, you will carefully bend to the other side. Finally, you will return to the center, lower your arms, and rest your hands in your lap.

Technique Start:

We are going to practice "Seated Side Bend."

Sit up straight and comfortably in your chair.

Rest your hands on your desk or in your lap.

Feel your feet flat on the floor.

Relax your shoulders back and down.

Let your whole body be still.

Stretch your arms straight over your head with your palms facing each other.

Interlace your fingers and point your index fingers up.

Keep stretching up with your elbows straight.

Now, comfortably bend to one side.

Close your eyes or leave them open.

Hold your body still.

Feel the stretch in the side of your body.

Take a deep breath in and exhale slowly.

Now, lift your body up, returning to the center.

Comfortably bend to the other side.

Hold your body still.

Feel the stretch in the side of your body.

SEATED SIDE BEND (cont.)

Take a deep breath in and exhale slowly.

Now, lift your body up, returning to the center.

Slowly lower your arms and rest your hands on your desk or in your lap.

Feel the air moving in and out of your nose.
[Wait 10 seconds]

Now, take a deep breath in, hold and exhale slowly.

Notice how you feel.
[Wait 10 seconds]

Open your eyes if they were closed.

STANDING SIDE BEND

Introduction – Modeling:

We are going to practice a Calm Classroom technique today called "Standing Side Bend." While standing upright next to your desk with your feet together, you will raise your arms above your head with your fingers interlaced and your index fingers pointing upward, like this *[teacher demonstrates]*. Then you will carefully bend to one side. *[Teacher demonstrates.]* Next, you will straighten your back and return to the center. *[Teacher demonstrates.]* Then, you will carefully bend to the other side. Finally, you will return to the center, lower your arms, and rest your hands by your sides.

Technique Start:

We are going to practice "Standing Side Bend."

Stand up straight and comfortably with your feet together.

Feel your feet flat on the floor.

Rest your arms by your sides.

Relax your shoulders back and down.

Let your whole body be still.

Stretch your arms straight over your head with your palms facing each other.

Interlace your fingers and extend your index fingers up.

Keep stretching up with your elbows straight.

Now, comfortably bend to one side.

Close your eyes or leave them open.

Hold your body still.

Feel the stretch in the side of your body.

Take a deep breath in and exhale slowly.

Now, lift your body up, returning to the center.

STANDING SIDE BEND (cont.)

Comfortably bend to the other side.

Hold your body still.

Feel the stretch in the side of your body.

Take a deep breath in and exhale slowly.

Now, lift your body up, returning to the center.

Slowly lower your arms and rest your hands by your sides.

Feel the air moving in and out of your nose.
[Wait 20-30 seconds]

Now, take a deep breath in, hold and exhale slowly.

Notice how you feel.
[Wait 10 seconds]

Open your eyes if they were closed.

SEATED TWIST

Introduction – Modeling:

We are going to practice a Calm Classroom technique today called "Seated Twist." While sitting upright in your chair, place your right hand close behind you and your left hand on your right leg, like this *[teacher demonstrates]*. Then you will twist to the right while looking over your right shoulder. *[Teacher demonstrates.]* Next, you will unwind your back and return to the center. *[Teacher demonstrates.]* Then, you will place your left hand close behind you and your right hand on your left leg, like this *[teacher demonstrates]*. Then you will twist to the left while looking over your left shoulder. *[Teacher demonstrates.]* Finally, you will unwind your back and return to the center, and rest your hands back in your lap. *[Teacher demonstrates.]*

Technique Start:

We are going to practice "Seated Twist."

Sit up straight and comfortably in your chair.

Rest your hands on your desk or in your lap.

Feel your feet flat on the floor.

Relax your shoulders back and down.

Let your whole body be still.
[Wait 10 seconds]

Feel the air moving in and out of your nose.
[Wait 10 seconds]

Place your right hand close behind you and your left hand on your right leg, twist from your waist to the right.

Look over your right shoulder.

Close your eyes or leave them open.

Take a deep breath in and exhale slowly.

Keep your back straight and relax your shoulders down.

SEATED TWIST (cont.)

Feel the air moving in and out of your nose.

Notice the feeling in your body as you hold your twist.

Now, turn your upper body back to the center.

Place your left hand close behind you and your right hand on your left leg, twist from your waist to the left.

Look over your left shoulder.

Take a deep breath in and exhale slowly.

Keep your back straight and relax your shoulders down.

Feel the air moving in and out of your nose.

Notice the feeling in your body as you hold your twist.

Now, turn your upper body back to the center.

Rest your hands on your desk or in your lap.

Feel the air moving in and out of your nose.
[Wait 20-30 seconds]

Now, take a deep breath in, hold and exhale slowly.

Notice how you feel.
[Wait 10 seconds]

Open your eyes if they were closed.

STANDING BODY CIRCLES

Introduction – Modeling:

We are going to practice a Calm Classroom technique today called "Standing Body Circles." You are going to move different parts of your body in a circular motion. You will stand up straight next to your desk with your feet together and your arms by your sides. You will start by moving your head slowly to the right, then down, then left, then center. *[Teacher demonstrates.]* Then, you will circle your head in the opposite direction. Next, you will put your hands on the top of your shoulders, with your elbows pointed out, like this *[teacher demonstrates]*. You will rotate your shoulders forward, and then backward. Next, you will put your arms out in front of you, like this *[teacher demonstrates]*. You will be circling your wrists outward and inward. *[Teacher demonstrates.]* Finally, you will bend your knees, place your hands on your knees, and move your knees in circles both to the right and left. *[Teacher demonstrates.]*

Technique Start:

We are going to practice "Standing Body Circles."

Stand up straight and comfortably with your feet together.

Rest your arms by your sides.

Close your eyes or leave them open.

Feel your feet flat on the floor.

Relax your shoulders back and down.

Let your whole body be still.

Now, slowly circle your head to the right, down, left and center.

Right, down, left, and center.

Right, down, left, and center.

Now, change directions and slowly circle your head to the left, down, right and center.

Left, down, right, and center.

STANDING BODY CIRCLES (cont.)

Left, down, right, and center.

Place your hands on the tops of your shoulders with your elbows pointed straight out to your sides.

Slowly circle your elbows and shoulders forward four times. 1, 2, 3, 4.

Slowly circle your elbows and shoulders back four times. 1, 2, 3, 4.

Now, reach your arms out in front of you.

Slowly circle your wrists outward four times. 1, 2, 3, 4.

Slowly circle your wrists inward four times. 1, 2, 3, 4.

Lower your arms by your sides.

Keep your feet together, bend your knees and place your hands on your knees.

Slowly circle your knees to the right four times. 1, 2, 3, 4.

Slowly circle your knees to the left four times. 1, 2, 3, 4.

Stand up straight and rest your arms by your sides.

Feel the air moving in and out of your nose.
[Wait 20-30 seconds]

Now, take a deep breath in, hold and exhale slowly.

Notice how you feel.
[Wait 10 seconds]

Open your eyes if they were closed.

SEATED BODY CIRCLES

Introduction – Modeling:

We are going to practice a Calm Classroom technique today called "Seated Body Circles." You are going to move different parts of your body in a circular motion. While sitting up straight in your chair, you will start by moving your head slowly to the right, then down, then left, then center. *[Teacher demonstrates.]* Then, you will circle your head in the opposite direction. Next, you will put your hands on the top of your shoulders, with your elbows pointed out, like this *[teacher demonstrates]*. You will rotate your shoulders forward, and then backward. Next, you will put your arms out in front of you, like this *[teacher demonstrates]*. You will be circling your wrists outward and inward. *[Teacher demonstrates.]*

Technique Start:

We are going to practice "Seated Body Circles."

Sit up straight and comfortably in your chair.

Rest your hands on your desk or in your lap.

Close your eyes or leave them open.

Feel your feet flat on the floor.

Relax your shoulders back and down.

Let your whole body be still.

Now, slowly circle your head to the right, down, left and center.

Right, down, left, and center.

Right, down, left, and center.

Now, change directions and slowly circle your head to the left, down, right and center.

Left, down, right, and center.

Left, down, right, and center.

SEATED BODY CIRCLES (cont.)

Place your hands on the tops of your shoulders with your elbows pointed straight out to your sides.

Slowly circle your elbows and shoulders forward four times. 1, 2, 3, 4.

Slowly circle your elbows and shoulders back four times. 1, 2, 3, 4.

Now, reach your arms out in front of you.

Slowly circle your wrists outward four times. 1, 2, 3, 4.

Slowly circle your wrists inward four times. 1, 2, 3, 4.

Slowly lower your arms and rest your hands on your desk or in your lap.

Feel the air moving in and out of your nose.
[Wait 20-30 seconds]

Now, take a deep breath in, hold and exhale slowly.

Notice how you feel.
[Wait 10 seconds]

Open your eyes if they were closed.

TEMPLATES

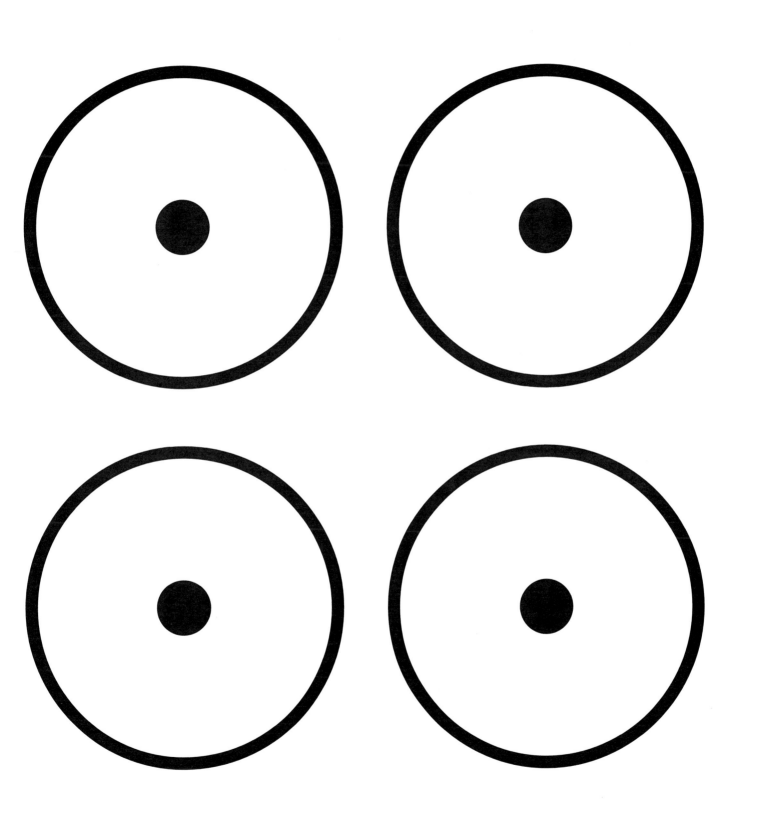